SCHOLASTIC

Do The Math™

Created by
Marilyn Burns

÷ Division Ⓑ

Facts through 100 ÷ 10

· ·

WorkSpace

Copyright © 2008 by Scholastic Inc.

All rights reserved.   Published by Scholastic Inc.   Printed in the U.S.A.

ISBN-13: 978-0-545-02250-7
ISBN-10: 0-545-02250-9

SCHOLASTIC, DO THE MATH, and associated logos and designs are trademarks and/or registered trademarks of Scholastic Inc.

1   2   3   4   5   6   7   8   9   10   40   16   15   14   13   12   11   10   09   08   07

Relay Teams with 24 Students

1

There are 24 students.

Each relay team has 3 students.

How many teams will they have? _____

Read the problem.

2

$24 \div 3 = \underline{8}$

$\underline{8} \times 3 = 24$

How many teams will they have? __8__

Write equations.
Answer the question.

3

Check your answer with tiles.

Problem	Equations
(1) There are 24 students. Each relay team has 4 students. How many teams will they have? _____	
(2) There are 24 students. Each relay team has 12 students. How many teams will they have? _____	
(3) There are 24 students. Each relay team has 8 students. How many teams will they have? _____	
(4) There are 24 students. Each relay team has 2 students. How many teams will they have? _____	

Home Note: Your child solves division problems by using multiplication, the inverse operation.

Relay Team Problems

1

There are 21 students.

Each relay team has 3 students.

How many teams will they have? _____

Read the problem.

2

$$21 \div 3 = \underline{7}$$
$$\underline{7} \times 3 = 21$$

How many teams will they have? __7__

Write equations.
Answer the question.

3

Check your answer with tiles.

Problem	Equations
(1) There are 18 students. Each relay team has 6 students. How many teams will they have? _____	
(2) There are 30 students. Each relay team has 5 students. How many teams will they have? _____	
(3) There are 15 students. Each relay team has 3 students. How many teams will they have? _____	
(4) There are 12 students. Each relay team has 6 students. How many teams will they have? _____	
(5) There are 25 students. Each relay team has 5 students. How many teams will they have? _____	

Home Note: Your child solves division problems by using multiplication, the inverse operation.

Relay Team Problems

1

There are 21 students.
Each team has 4 students.

Can they make teams with
no one left out? ___no___

How many teams will they have?
___5___

How many are left out? ___1___

2

$21 \div 4 = \underline{5\,R1}$
$5 \times 4 = 20$
$6 \times 4 = 24$

Write the division and
multiplication equations.
Answer the questions.

3

Check your answer
with tiles.

Problem	Equations
① There are 24 students. Each team has 10 students. Can they make teams with no one left out? _____ How many teams will they have? _____ How many are left out? _____	
② There are 18 students. Each team has 5 students. Can they make teams with no one left out? _____ How many teams will they have? _____ How many are left out? _____	
③ There are 25 students. Each team has 7 students. Can they make teams with no one left out? _____ How many teams will they have? _____ How many are left out? _____	
④ There are 28 students. Each team has 4 students. Can they make teams with no one left out? _____ How many teams will they have? _____ How many are left out? _____	

Home Note: Your child solves division problems with remainders.

Game Rules for Division Bingo A

What you need

- *Division Bingo* A card (*WorkSpace* page 7)
- number cube (1–6)
- pencil

➤ **The goal is to mark five boxes in a row—across, up and down, or from corner to corner. Players take turns.**

1

$$20$$

$$20 \div 4 = 5$$
$$5 \times 4 = 20$$

On your turn roll the number cube and choose a number on the *Division Bingo* card that is divisible by the number on the cube.

Then write a division equation and a multiplication equation.

2

Division Bingo Ⓐ

1	2	3	4	5
21	24	25	27	6
20	36	FREE SPACE	28	8
18	35	32	30	9
16	15	14	12	10

Mark an X on the number you chose.

3

Hand the cube to your partner.

Home Note: Your child plays a game that reinforces his or her understanding of divisibility.

Division Bingo

DIRECTIONS

1

Roll
4

Roll and record the number.

2

Dividend from Bingo Card
20

Choose a dividend and record.

3

Equations
$20 \div 4 = 5$ $5 \times 4 = 20$

Write a division and a multiplication equation.

Roll	Dividend from Bingo Card	Equations	Roll	Dividend from Bingo Card	Equations

Home Note: Your child plays a game that reinforces his or her understanding of divisibility.

Division Bingo Ⓐ

1	2	3	4	5
21	24	25	27	6
20	36	FREE SPACE	28	8
18	35	32	30	9
16	15	14	12	10

Home Note: Your child plays a game that reinforces his or her understanding of divisibility.

Division Bingo

DIRECTIONS

1

Roll

4

Roll and record the number.

2

Dividend from Bingo Card

20

Choose a dividend and record.

3

Equations

$20 \div 4 = 5$
$5 \times 4 = 20$

Write a division and a multiplication equation.

Roll	Dividend from Bingo Card	Equations

Roll	Dividend from Bingo Card	Equations

Home Note: Your child plays a game that reinforces his or her understanding of divisibility.

Division Bingo Ⓐ

1	2	3	4	5
21	24	25	27	6
20	36	FREE SPACE	28	8
18	35	32	30	9
16	15	14	12	10

Home Note: Your child plays a game that reinforces his or her understanding of divisibility.

Show What You Know

➤ Write the division problem.

➤ Write the multiplication equation or equations.

➤ Fill in the answers.

Problem	Equations
1 There are 27 students. Each team has 9 students. Can they make teams with no one left out? _____ How many teams will they have? _____ How many are left out? _____	
2 There are 18 students. Each team has 4 students. Can they make teams with no one left out? _____ How many teams will they have? _____ How many are left out? _____	
3 There are 30 students. Each team has 7 students. Can they make teams with no one left out? _____ How many teams will they have? _____ How many are left out? _____	

Home Note: Your child solves division problems with and without remainders.

➤ For each roll, choose a dividend and record.

➤ Write a division and a multiplication equation.

➤ Mark the dividend with an X.

Division Bingo Ⓐ

1	2	3	4	5
21	24	25	27	6
20	36	FREE SPACE	28	8
18	35	32	30	9
16	15	14	12	10

Roll	Dividend from Bingo Card	Equations
④ 4		
⑤ 6		

Home Note: Your child writes division and multiplication equations for a division problem.

Division Bingo

DIRECTIONS

1

Roll
4

Roll and record the number.

2

Dividend from Bingo Card
20

Choose a dividend and record.

3

Equations
$20 \div 4 = 5$ $5 \times 4 = 20$

Write a division and a multiplication equation.

Roll	Dividend from Bingo Card	Equations	Roll	Dividend from Bingo Card	Equations

Home Note: Your child plays a game that reinforces his or her understanding of divisibility.

Division Bingo Ⓐ

1	2	3	4	5
21	24	25	27	6
20	36	FREE SPACE	28	8
18	35	32	30	9
16	15	14	12	10

Home Note: Your child plays a game that reinforces his or her understanding of divisibility.

Division Bingo

DIRECTIONS

1

Roll
4

Roll and record the number.

2

Dividend from Bingo Card
20

Choose a dividend and record.

3

Equations
$20 \div 4 = 5$ $5 \times 4 = 20$

Write a division and a multiplication equation.

Roll	Dividend from Bingo Card	Equations	Roll	Dividend from Bingo Card	Equations

Home Note: Your child plays a game that reinforces his or her understanding of divisibility.

Division Bingo Ⓐ

1	2	3	4	5
21	24	25	27	6
20	36	FREE SPACE	28	8
18	35	32	30	9
16	15	14	12	10

Home Note: Your child plays a game that reinforces his or her understanding of divisibility.

Sharing Problems

1

28 tiles

4 people

How many tiles will
each person get? ___7___

Read the problem.

2

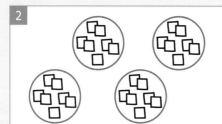

Draw circles and use tiles
to solve the problem.

3

$4 \times 7 = 28$

$28 \div 4 = 7$

Write the multiplication
and division equations.
Answer the question.

---

(1) 32 tiles

4 people

How many tiles
will each
person get?

_____

---

(2) 35 tiles

5 people

How many tiles
will each
person get?

_____

---

(3) 24 tiles

3 people

How many tiles
will each
person get?

_____

Home Note: Your child uses tiles and multiplication to solve sharing division problems.

7 People Sharing 40 Tiles

DIRECTIONS

44 tiles

8 people

1

8 × ___ is close to 40.

$$8 \times 5 = 40$$
$$8 \times 6 = 48$$

Write multiplication equations.

2

$$44 \div 8 = 5\,R4$$

Write a division equation.

3

Is 44 divisible by 8?

no

How do you know?

The remainder is 4.

Answer the questions.

	Multiplication equations	Division equation	Divisible?
40 tiles **7 people**	7 × _____ is close to 40.		Is 40 divisible by 7? _____ How do you know? _____ _____ _____

Home Note: Your child uses tiles and multiplication to solve a sharing division problem with a remainder.

Solving Sharing Problems with Multiplication

DIRECTIONS

44 tiles

8 people

1 8 × ____ is close to 40.

$$8 \times 5 = 40$$
$$8 \times 6 = 48$$

Write multiplication equations.

2 $44 \div 8 = 5\,R4$

Write a division equation.

3 Is 44 divisible by 8?

no

How do you know?

The remainder is 4.

Answer the questions.

	Multiplication equations	Division equation	Divisible?
1 35 tiles 8 people	8 × ____ is close to 35.		Is 35 divisible by 8? ____ How do you know? ____ ____ ____
2 32 tiles 7 people	7 × ____ is close to 32.		Is 32 divisible by 7? ____ How do you know? ____ ____ ____
3 36 tiles 5 people	5 × ____ is close to 36.		Is 36 divisible by 5? ____ How do you know? ____ ____

Home Note: Your child uses multiplication to solve sharing division problems with remainders.

Which Rolls Will Work?

Division Bingo Ⓐ

1	2	3	4	5
21	24	25	27	6
(20)	36	FREE SPACE	28	8
18	35	32	30	9
16	15	14	12	10

1

$20 \div 1 =$
$20 \div 2 =$
$20 \div 3 =$
$20 \div 4 =$
$20 \div 5 =$
$20 \div 6 =$

Write the division problems.

2

$20 \div 1 = 20$
$20 \div 2 = 10$
$20 \div 3 = 6\,R2$
$20 \div 4 = 5$
$20 \div 5 = 4$
$20 \div 6 = 3\,R2$

Solve the division problems.

3

Which rolls will work?

_1, 2, 4, 5_

Answer the question.

---

①

Division Bingo Ⓐ

1	2	3	4	5
21	24	25	27	(6)
20	36	FREE SPACE	28	8
18	35	32	30	9
16	15	14	12	10

Which rolls will work?

_____

②

Division Bingo Ⓐ

1	2	3	4	5
21	24	25	27	6
20	36	FREE SPACE	28	8
18	35	32	30	9
16	(15)	14	12	10

Which rolls will work?

_____

③

Division Bingo Ⓐ

1	2	3	4	5
21	(24)	25	27	6
20	36	FREE SPACE	28	8
18	35	32	30	9
16	15	14	12	10

Which rolls will work?

_____

Home Note: Your child uses division to determine which divisors give zero remainders.

Division Bingo

DIRECTIONS

1

Roll
4

Roll and record the number.

2

Dividend from Bingo Card
20

Choose a dividend and record.

3

Equations
$20 \div 4 = 5$ $5 \times 4 = 20$

Write a division and a multiplication equation.

Roll	Dividend from Bingo Card	Equations	Roll	Dividend from Bingo Card	Equations

Home Note: Your child plays a game that reinforces his or her understanding of divisibility.

Division Bingo Ⓐ

1	2	3	4	5
21	24	25	27	6
20	36	FREE SPACE	28	8
18	35	32	30	9
16	15	14	12	10

Home Note: Your child plays a game that reinforces his or her understanding of divisibility.

Division Bingo

1

Roll
4

Roll and record the number.

2

Dividend from Bingo Card
20

Choose a dividend and record.

3

Equations
$20 \div 4 = 5$ $5 \times 4 = 20$

Write a division and a multiplication equation.

Roll	Dividend from Bingo Card	Equations	Roll	Dividend from Bingo Card	Equations

Lesson 9   **Home Note:** Your child plays a game that reinforces his or her understanding of divisibility.

Division Bingo Ⓐ

1	2	3	4	5
21	24	25	27	6
20	36	FREE SPACE	28	8
18	35	32	30	9
16	15	14	12	10

Home Note: Your child plays a game that reinforces his or her understanding of divisibility.

Show What You Know

➤ Write the multiplication equations.

➤ Write the division equations.

➤ Answer the questions.

	Multiplication equations	Division equation	Divisible?
① 27 tiles 6 people	$6 \times \underline{\quad} = 27$		Is 27 divisible by 6? _____ How do you know? _____ _____ _____
② 25 tiles 3 people	$3 \times \underline{\quad} = 25$		Is 25 divisible by 3? _____ How do you know? _____ _____ _____
③ 33 tiles 4 people	$4 \times \underline{\quad} = 33$		Is 33 divisible by 4? _____ How do you know? _____ _____ _____
④ 28 tiles 5 people	$5 \times \underline{\quad} = 28$		Is 28 divisible by 5? _____ How do you know? _____ _____ _____

Home Note: Your child uses multiplication to solve sharing division problems with remainders.

➤ Figure out numbers divisible by 3 and 4.

➤ Write a multiplication and division equation for each.

➤ Circle the numbers.

Figure out 3 numbers divisible by 3.
Write a multiplication and division equation for each.
Circle each number.

⑤ _____

_____

⑥ _____

_____

⑦ _____

_____

Division Bingo Ⓐ

1	2	3	4	5
21	24	25	27	6
20	36	FREE SPACE	28	8
18	35	32	30	9
16	15	14	12	10

Figure out 3 numbers divisible by 4.
Write a multiplication and division equation for each.
Circle each number.

⑧ _____

_____

⑨ _____

_____

⑩ _____

_____

Division Bingo Ⓐ

1	2	3	4	5
21	24	25	27	6
20	36	FREE SPACE	28	8
18	35	32	30	9
16	15	14	12	10

Home Note: Your child writes division equations and multiplication equations for given pairs of numbers.

Division Bingo

DIRECTIONS

1

Roll
4

Roll and record the number.

2

Dividend from Bingo Card
20

Choose a dividend and record.

3

Equations
$20 \div 4 = 5$ $5 \times 4 = 20$

Write a division and a multiplication equation.

Roll	Dividend from Bingo Card	Equations

Roll	Dividend from Bingo Card	Equations

Home Note: Your child plays a game that reinforces his or her understanding of divisibility.

Division Bingo Ⓐ

1	2	3	4	5
21	24	25	27	6
20	36	FREE SPACE	28	8
18	35	32	30	9
16	15	14	12	10

Home Note: Your child plays a game that reinforces his or her understanding of divisibility.

100 Hungry Ants

➤ Write multiplication equations for the arrangement.

1 ••

1 row of 100 ants   100 rows, with 1 ant in each row

_____   _____

2 ••••••••••••••••••••••••••••••••••••
••••••••••••••••••••••••••••••••••

2 rows, with 50 ants in each row   50 rows, with 2 ants in each row

_____   _____

3 •••••••••••••••••••••••••
•••••••••••••••••••••••••
•••••••••••••••••••••••••

4 rows, with 25 ants in each row   25 rows, with 4 ants in each row

_____   _____

4 ••••••••••••••••••••
••••••••••••••••••••
••••••••••••••••••••
••••••••••••••••••••

5 rows, with 20 ants in each row   20 rows, with 5 ants in each row

_____   _____

5 ••••••••••
••••••••••
••••••••••
••••••••••
••••••••••
••••••••••
••••••••••
••••••••••
••••••••••
••••••••••

10 rows, with 10 ants in each row

_____

🏠 **Home Note:** Your child writes multiplication equations for formations of 100 ants.

100 Hungry Ants in Equal Rows

➤ Write division and multiplication equations for the arrangements.

1

•••
•••

100 ants in 2 rows of 50

_____ _____

_____ _____

2

••••••••••••••••••••••••
••••••••••••••••••••••••
••••••••••••••••••••••••
••••••••••••••••••••••••

100 ants in 4 rows of 25

_____ _____

_____ _____

3

••••••••••••••••••••
••••••••••••••••••••
••••••••••••••••••••
••••••••••••••••••••
••••••••••••••••••••

100 ants in 5 rows of 20

_____ _____

_____ _____

4

••••••••••
••••••••••
••••••••••
••••••••••
••••••••••
••••••••••
••••••••••
••••••••••
••••••••••
••••••••••

100 ants in 10 rows of 10

_____ _____

Home Note: Your child writes division equations for formations of 100 ants.

Division Bingo

1

Roll
4

Roll and record the number.

2

Dividend from Bingo Card
20

Choose a dividend and record.

3

Equations
$20 \div 4 = 5$ $5 \times 4 = 20$

Write a division and a multiplication equation.

Roll	Dividend from Bingo Card	Equations

Roll	Dividend from Bingo Card	Equations

Home Note: Your child plays a game that reinforces his or her understanding of divisibility.

Division Bingo Ⓐ

1	2	3	4	5
21	24	25	27	6
20	36	FREE SPACE	28	8
18	35	32	30	9
16	15	14	12	10

Home Note: Your child plays a game that reinforces his or her understanding of divisibility.

20 Tiles in Equal Rows

1

5 in each row

Try to arrange the 20 tiles in equal rows with 1, 2, 3, 4, 5, 6, . . . up to 20 in each row.

2

$4 \times 5 = 20$ $20 \div 4 = 5$

$5 \times 4 = 20$ $20 \div 5 = 4$

Write two multiplication and two division equations for arrangements of equal rows with no leftovers.

3

7 in each row

7

If an arrangement has tiles left over, write the number of tiles you put in each row in the box at the bottom of the page.

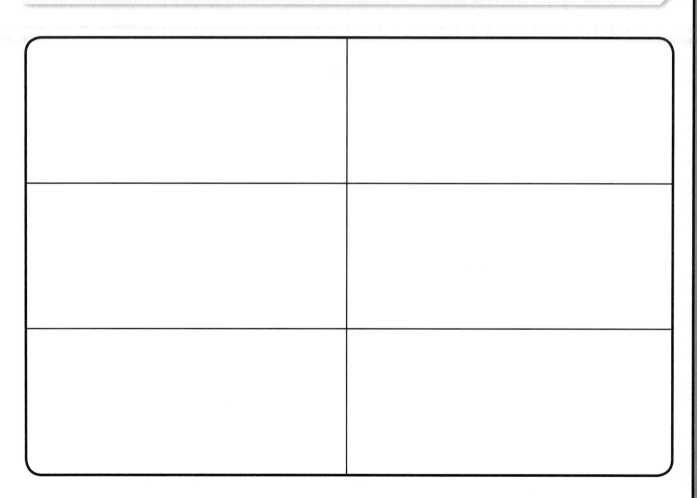

Numbers that have leftovers

Home Note: Your child makes arrangements of 20 tiles and writes multiplication and division equations.

30 Tiles

1

5 in each row

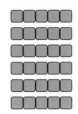

Try to arrange the 30 tiles in equal rows with 1, 2, 3, 4, 5, 6, . . . up to 30 in each row.

2

$6 \times 5 = 30$ $30 \div 6 = 5$

$5 \times 6 = 30$ $30 \div 5 = 6$

Write two multiplication and two division equations for arrangements of equal rows with no leftovers.

3

7 in each row

7

If an arrangement has tiles left over, write the number of tiles you put in each row in the box at the bottom of the page.

Numbers that have leftovers

Home Note: Your child makes arrangements of 30 tiles and writes multiplication and division equations.

Division Bingo

1

Roll
7

Roll and record the number.

2

Dividend from Bingo Card
35

Choose a dividend and record.

3

Equations
$35 \div 7 = 5$ $5 \times 7 = 35$

Write a division and a multiplication equation.

Roll	Dividend from Bingo Card	Equations	Roll	Dividend from Bingo Card	Equations

34   Lesson 14   **Home Note:** Your child plays a game that reinforces his or her understanding of divisibility.

Division Bingo Ⓑ

25	48	35
54	40	45
63	72	42

Home Note: Your child plays a game that reinforces his or her understanding of divisibility.

Division Bingo

DIRECTIONS

1

Roll
7

Roll and record the number.

2

Dividend from Bingo Card
49

Choose a dividend and record.

3

Equations
$49 \div 7 = 7$ $7 \times 7 = 49$

Write a division and a multiplication equation.

Roll	Dividend from Bingo Card	Equations	Roll	Dividend from Bingo Card	Equations

Home Note: Your child plays a game that reinforces his or her understanding of divisibility.

Division Bingo C

40	30	56
49	72	45
48	35	63

Home Note: Your child plays a game that reinforces his or her understanding of divisibility.

Lesson 14

37

Division Bingo

DIRECTIONS

1

Roll
7

Roll and record the number.

2

Dividend from Bingo Card
35

Choose a dividend and record.

3

Equations
$35 \div 7 = 5$ $5 \times 7 = 35$

Write a division and a multiplication equation.

Roll	Dividend from Bingo Card	Equations

Roll	Dividend from Bingo Card	Equations

Home Note: Your child plays a game that reinforces his or her understanding of divisibility.

Division Bingo Ⓑ

25	48	35
54	40	45
63	72	42

Home Note: Your child plays a game that reinforces his or her understanding of divisibility.

Show What You Know

DIRECTIONS

➤ Try to arrange 24 tiles in equal rows of 1 tile, 2 tiles, 3 tiles, 4 tiles, and so on. Draw each arrangement that has no leftovers.

➤ Write two multiplication and two division equations for each arrangement that has no leftovers.

Home Note: Your child makes arrangements of 24 tiles and writes multiplication and division equations.

> ➤ **Write the numbers that make arrangements with leftovers in the box below. Complete the sentence.**

Numbers that make arrangements with leftovers

24 is divisible by _____ .

 Home Note: Your child makes arrangements of 24 tiles and writes multiplication and division equations.

Division Bingo

DIRECTIONS

1

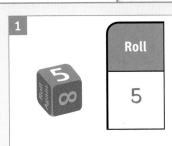

Roll
5

Roll and record the number.

2

Dividend from Bingo Card
30

Choose a dividend and record.

3

Equations
$30 \div 5 = 6$ $6 \times 5 = 30$

Write a division and a multiplication equation.

Roll	Dividend from Bingo Card	Equations

Roll	Dividend from Bingo Card	Equations

Lesson 15 🏠 **Home Note:** Your child plays a game that reinforces his or her understanding of divisibility.

Division Bingo Ⓓ

56	42	36
40	54	81
64	30	48

Home Note: Your child plays a game that reinforces his or her understanding of divisibility.

Divide by 2

DIRECTIONS

1

$56 \div 2 =$

$56 = 50 + 6$

Split the dividend
into tens and ones.

2

$50 \div 2 = 25$

$6 \div 2 = 3$

Divide the tens.
Divide the ones.

3

$25 + 3 = 28$

$56 \div 2 = 28$

Add the quotients.
Write the answer.

① $94 \div 2 =$

② $72 \div 2 =$

③ $48 \div 2 =$

④ $34 \div 2 =$

⑤ $56 \div 2 =$

⑥ $58 \div 2 =$

⑦ $52 \div 2 =$

⑧ $96 \div 2 =$

Home Note: Your child splits two-digit numbers
into tens and ones to divide them by 2.

Divide by 5

1

$85 \div 5 =$

$85 = 50 + 35$

Split the dividend.

2

$50 \div 5 = 10$

$35 \div 5 = 7$

Divide the two addends.

3

$10 + 7 = 17$

$85 \div 5 = 17$

Add the quotients.
Write the answer.

---

① $75 \div 5 =$

② $70 \div 5 =$

③ $80 \div 5 =$

④ $85 \div 5 =$

⑤ $65 \div 5 =$

⑥ $90 \div 5 =$

⑦ $95 \div 5 =$

⑧ $60 \div 5 =$

Home Note: Your child uses a splitting strategy to divide numbers by 5.

Divide by 10

➤ Write the answer for the division problems.

EXAMPLE

$85 \div 10 = 8 \text{ R}5$

① $75 \div 10 =$	② $89 \div 10 =$
③ $67 \div 10 =$	④ $58 \div 10 =$
⑤ $95 \div 10 =$	⑥ $64 \div 10 =$
⑦ $72 \div 10 =$	⑧ $60 \div 10 =$
⑨ $91 \div 10 =$	⑩ $80 \div 10 =$

Home Note: Your child divides two-digit numbers by 10.

Show What You Know

➤ Write the answer.

➤ If you use splitting, write the equations to show how you solved the problem.

① $96 \div 2 =$

② $69 \div 10 =$

③ $85 \div 5 =$

④ $65 \div 5 =$

⑤ $78 \div 10 =$

⑥ $84 \div 10 =$

⑦ $72 \div 2 =$

⑧ $54 \div 2 =$

⑨ $90 \div 5 =$

⑩ $90 \div 10 =$

Home Note: Your child divides two-digit numbers by 2, 5, and 10.

Division Bingo

DIRECTIONS

1

Roll

7

Roll and record the number.

2

Dividend from Bingo Card

49

Choose a dividend and record.

3

Equations

$49 \div 7 = 7$
$7 \times 7 = 49$

Write a division and a multiplication equation.

Roll	Dividend from Bingo Card	Equations	Roll	Dividend from Bingo Card	Equations

Lesson 20

Home Note: Your child plays a game that reinforces his or her understanding of divisibility.

Division Bingo **C**

40	30	56
49	72	45
48	35	63

Home Note: Your child plays a game that reinforces his or her understanding of divisibility.

Lesson 20

49

Division Bingo

DIRECTIONS

1

Roll
7

Roll and record the number.

2

Dividend from Bingo Card
35

Choose a dividend and record.

3

Equations
$35 \div 7 = 5$ $5 \times 7 = 35$

Write a division and a multiplication equation.

Roll	Dividend from Bingo Card	Equations

Roll	Dividend from Bingo Card	Equations

Lesson 20

Home Note: Your child plays a game that reinforces his or her understanding of divisibility.

Division Bingo **D**

56	42	36
40	54	81
64	30	48

Home Note: Your child plays a game that reinforces his or her understanding of divisibility.

Solve Relay Problems

DIRECTIONS

There are 20 students. Each team has 4 students.

How many teams can they make?

1

$4)\overline{20}$

Write the problem. Solve with tiles if you want.

2

$$4)\overline{20}$$ with 5 on top, $\underline{20}$ below, 0 remainder

$5 \times 4 = 20$

Solve with long division.

3

Can they make teams with no one left out? ___yes___

How many teams can they make? ___5___

Answer the questions.

1 There are 30 students. Each team has 6 students. How many teams can they make?		Can they make teams with no one left out? _____ How many teams can they make? _____
2 There are 32 students. Each team has 8 students. How many teams can they make?		Can they make teams with no one left out? _____ How many teams can they make? _____
3 There are 28 students. Each team has 4 students. How many teams can they make?		Can they make teams with no one left out? _____ How many teams can they make? _____
4 There are 35 students. Each team has 5 students. How many teams can they make?		Can they make teams with no one left out? _____ How many teams can they make? _____

Home Note: Your child uses long division notation to solve division problems.

Solve More Relay Problems

DIRECTIONS

There are 23 students.
Each team has 4 students.

How many teams can they make?

1

$4\overline{)23}$

Write the problem. Solve with tiles if you want.

2

$\begin{array}{r} 5\,R3 \\ 4\overline{)23} \\ \underline{20} \\ 3 \end{array}$ $5 \times 4 = 20$

Solve with long division.

3

Can they make teams with no one left out? __no__

How many teams can they make? __5__

Answer the questions.

---

1 There are 28 students. Each team has 5 students.

How many teams can they make?

Can they make teams with no one left out? _____

How many teams can they make? _____

---

2 There are 34 students. Each team has 4 students.

How many teams can they make?

Can they make teams with no one left out? _____

How many teams can they make? _____

---

3 There are 20 students. Each team has 6 students.

How many teams can they make?

Can they make teams with no one left out? _____

How many teams can they make? _____

---

4 There are 30 students. Each team has 7 students.

How many teams can they make?

Can they make teams with no one left out? _____

How many teams can they make? _____

Home Note: Your child writes related multiplication equations and uses long division notation to solve division problems with remainders.

Long Division Practice

1

$4\overline{)52}$

$$\begin{array}{r} 10 \\ 4\overline{)52} \\ 40 \\ \hline 12 \end{array}$$

$10 \times 4 = 40$

Write a multiplication equation.

2

$$\begin{array}{r} 3 \\ 10 \end{array} \Big\rangle 13$$

$$\begin{array}{r} 4\overline{)52} \\ 40 \\ \hline 12 \\ 12 \\ \hline 0 \end{array}$$

$10 \times 4 = 40$

$3 \times 4 = 12$

Write the division.

3

$$\begin{array}{r} 13 \\ \times 4 \\ \hline 52 \end{array}$$

Check the answer.

$4\overline{)61}$

Lesson 23

Home Note: Your child uses long division notation to solve a division problem with a remainder.

More Long Division Practice

1

$$3\overline{)47}$$

$$\begin{array}{r} 10 \\ 3\overline{)47} \\ 30 \\ \hline 17 \end{array} \quad 10 \times 3 = 30$$

Write a multiplication equation.

2

$$\begin{array}{r} 5 \\ 10 \\ 3\overline{)47} \\ 30 \\ \hline 17 \\ 15 \\ \hline 2 \end{array} \quad \begin{array}{l} 15\,R2 \\ \\ 10 \times 3 = 30 \\ \\ 5 \times 3 = 15 \end{array}$$

Write the division.

3

$$\begin{array}{r} 15 \\ \times 3 \\ \hline 45 \\ + 2 \\ \hline 47 \end{array}$$

Check the answers.

1

$$5\overline{)65}$$

2

$$3\overline{)54}$$

3

$$6\overline{)75}$$

4

$$4\overline{)68}$$

Home Note: Your child uses long division notation to solve division problems with and without remainders.

Lesson 23

55

Number Cube Problems

$34 \div 5 = 6\ R4$

$35 \div 4 = 8\ R3$

$45 \div 3 = 15\ R0$

$43 \div 5 = 8\ R3$

$54 \div 3 = 18\ R0$

$53 \div 4 = $ _____

DIRECTIONS

➤ Solve and fill in the blank above.

$$4\overline{)53}$$

Home Note: Your child uses long division notation to solve a division problem with a remainder.

Remainder Zero

1

Roll three number cubes.

2

If any numbers are the same, roll one of the cubes with the same number again. You need three different numbers.

3

$34 \div 5 = 6\,R4$
$43 \div 5 = 8\,R3$
$53 \div 4 = 13\,R1$
$54 \div 3 = 18\,R0$
$45 \div 3 = 15\,R0$
$35 \div 4 = 8\,R3$

Write six division problems. Solve them.

4

Number of zero remainders ☐ 2

Record the number of zero remainders you have.

Numbers

Write six problems and solve. Use space below to solve.

① _____

② _____

③ _____

④ _____

⑤ _____

⑥ _____

Number of zero remainders ☐

Solve here.

Home Note: Your child plays a game that gives him or her practice dividing two-digit numbers.

Game Rules for Remainder Zero

What you need

- three number cubes (1–6)
- *WorkSpace* page 57
- pencil

➤ **One pair plays against another pair.**

1

Roll the three number cubes. If any numbers
are the same, roll one of the cubes with the
same number again until you have three
different numbers. Record the three numbers.

2

$34 \div 2$
$32 \div 4$
$24 \div 3$
$23 \div 4$
$42 \div 3$
$43 \div 2$

Write 6 problems.

3

$34 \div 2 = 17 \text{ R0}$
$32 \div 4 = 8 \text{ R0}$
$24 \div 3 = 8 \text{ R0}$
$23 \div 4 = 5 \text{ R3}$
$42 \div 3 = 14 \text{ R0}$
$43 \div 2 = 21 \text{ R1}$

Solve each problem.

4

4

Record your number
of zero remainders.

➤ **The pair with the greater number of zero remainders wins.**

Home Note: Your child plays a game that gives
him or her practice dividing two-digit numbers.

Show What You Know

➤ **Solve and check answers.**

①
$$7\overline{)45}$$

②
$$5\overline{)79}$$

③
$$6\overline{)72}$$

④
$$3\overline{)57}$$

⑤
$$4\overline{)70}$$

⑥
$$6\overline{)85}$$

Home Note: Your child uses long division notation to solve division problems with and without remainders.

Division Bingo

DIRECTIONS

1

Roll
7

Roll and record the number.

2

Dividend from Bingo Card
49

Choose a dividend and record.

3

Equations
$49 \div 7 = 7$
$7 \times 7 = 49$

Write a division and a multiplication equation.

Roll	Dividend from Bingo Card	Equations	Roll	Dividend from Bingo Card	Equations

Home Note: Your child plays a game that reinforces his or her understanding of divisibility.

Division Bingo C

40	30	56
49	72	45
48	35	63

Home Note: Your child plays a game that reinforces his or her understanding of divisibility.

Division Bingo

1

Roll
5

Roll and record the number.

2

Dividend from Bingo Card
30

Choose a dividend and record.

3

Equations
$30 \div 5 = 6$ $6 \times 5 = 30$

Write a division and a multiplication equation.

Roll	Dividend from Bingo Card	Equations		Roll	Dividend from Bingo Card	Equations

Home Note: Your child plays a game that reinforces his or her understanding of divisibility.

Division Bingo **D**

56	42	36
40	54	81
64	30	48

Home Note: Your child plays a game that reinforces his or her understanding of divisibility.

Remainder Zero

1

Roll three number cubes.

2

If any numbers are the same, roll one of the cubes with the same number again. You need three different numbers.

3

$34 \div 5 = 6\,R4$
$43 \div 5 = 8\,R3$
$53 \div 4 = 13\,R1$
$54 \div 3 = 18\,R0$
$45 \div 3 = 15\,R0$
$35 \div 4 = 8\,R3$

Write six division problems. Solve them.

4

Number of zero remainders [2]

Record the number of zero remainders you have.

Numbers

Write six problems and solve. Use space below to solve.

(1) _____

(2) _____

(3) _____

(4) _____

(5) _____

(6) _____

Number of zero remainders [ ]

Solve here.

Lesson 26

Home Note: Your child plays a game that gives him or her practice dividing two-digit numbers.

Remainder Zero

1

Roll three number cubes.

2

If any numbers are the same, roll one of the cubes with the same number again. You need three different numbers.

3

$34 \div 5 = 6\,R4$
$43 \div 5 = 8\,R3$
$53 \div 4 = 13\,R1$
$54 \div 3 = 18\,R0$
$45 \div 3 = 15\,R0$
$35 \div 4 = 8\,R3$

Write six division problems. Solve them.

4

Number of zero remainders ☐2☐

Record the number of zero remainders you have.

Numbers ☐ ☐ ☐

Write six problems and solve. Use space below to solve.

① _____

② _____

③ _____

④ _____

⑤ _____

⑥ _____

Number of zero remainders ☐

Solve here.

Home Note: Your child plays a game that gives him or her practice dividing two-digit numbers.

Division Bingo

DIRECTIONS

1

Roll
4

Roll and record the number.

2

Dividend from Bingo Card
24

Choose a dividend and record.

3

Equations
$24 \div 4 = 6$ $6 \times 4 = 24$

Write a division and a multiplication equation.

Roll	Dividend from Bingo Card	Equations

Roll	Dividend from Bingo Card	Equations

Home Note: Your child plays a game that reinforces his or her understanding of divisibility.

Division Bingo **E**

16	24	28	32	40
36	42	48	49	54
56	60	FREE SPACE	63	64
70	72	80	81	90
100	36	60	24	24

Home Note: Your child plays a game that reinforces his or her understanding of divisibility.

Game Rules for Division Bingo E

What you need

- *WorkSpace* pages 66–68
- number cube (4, 6, 7, 8, 9, 10)
- pencil

➤ The goal is to make five boxes in a row — across, up or down, or from corner to corner.

➤ Players take turns. Decide who is X and who is O.

➤ No number can be marked with both an X and an O.

1

  $\boxed{81}$ $81 \div 9 = 9$
$9 \times 9 = 81$

On your turn roll the number cube and choose a number on the *Division Bingo* card that is divisible by the number on the cube. Then write a division equation and a multiplication equation.

2

Division Bingo Ⓔ

16	24	28	32	40
36	42	48	49	54
56	60	FREE SPACE	63	64
70	72	80	8̶1̶	90
100	36	60	24	24

Both players mark an X on their card for the turn.

3

  $\boxed{42}$

Division Bingo Ⓔ

16	24	28	32	40
36	㊷	48	49	54
56	60	FREE SPACE	63	64
70	72	80	8̶1̶	90
100	36	60	24	24

$42 \div 7 = 6$
$6 \times 7 = 42$

Hand the cube to your partner. Your partner takes a turn. Both players mark the turn with an O on their card.

Home Note: Your child plays a game that reinforces his or her understanding of divisibility.

Relay Team Choices

➤ Solve each problem and check.

➤ Decide which is the better choice.

---

1 There are 78 students.
Each relay team has 4 students.

Can they make teams so
that no one will be left out? _____

How many teams will they have? _____

---

2 There are 78 students.
Each relay team has 6 students.

Can they make teams so
that no one will be left out? _____

How many teams will they have? _____

---

3 Which is the better choice? Explain your answer.

_____

_____

Home Note: Your child divides two-digit numbers to determine
which divisor results in a quotient with no remainder.

Relay Team Problems

➤ Write and solve both pairs of the division problems. Check your answers.

➤ For each pair, decide which is the better choice—the one where no student is left out.

---

1 There are 68 students.
Each relay team has 6 students.

Can they make teams so
that no one will be left out? _____

How many teams will they have? _____

2 There are 68 students.
Each relay team has 4 students.

Can they make teams so
that no one will be left out? _____

How many teams will they have? _____

Which is the better choice?

---

3 There are 90 students.
Each relay team has 6 students.

Can they make teams so
that no one will be left out? _____

How many teams will they have? _____

4 There are 90 students.
Each relay team has 4 students.

Can they make teams so
that no one will be left out? _____

How many teams will they have? _____

Which is the better choice?

Lesson 28

Home Note: Your child divides two-digit numbers to determine
which divisor results in a quotient with no remainder.

Write About Division

➤ Tell about division with words, numbers, and pictures.

ABOUT DIVISION

Home Note: Your child writes about what he or she has learned about division.

Show What You Know

DIRECTIONS

➤ Write and solve both pairs of division problems. Check your answers.

➤ For each pair, decide which is the better choice—the one where no student is left out.

---

1 There are 98 students.
Each relay team has 6 students.

Can they make teams so
that no one will be left out? _____

How many teams will they have? _____

2 There are 98 students.
Each relay team has 7 students.

Can they make teams so
that no one will be left out? _____

How many teams will they have? _____

Which is the better choice?

---

3 There are 51 students.
Each relay team has 4 students.

Can they make teams so
that no one will be left out? _____

How many teams will they have? _____

4 There are 51 students.
Each relay team has 3 students.

Can they make teams so
that no one will be left out? _____

How many teams will they have? _____

Which is the better choice?

Home Note: Your child divides two-digit numbers to determine which divisor results in a quotient with no remainder.

Show What You Know

➤ **Solve and check.**

①

$$6\overline{)68}$$

②

$$5\overline{)54}$$

③

$$6\overline{)75}$$

④

$$4\overline{)56}$$

Home Note: Your child uses long division notation to solve division problems with and without remainders.

Show What You Know

DIRECTIONS

➤ Roll three number cubes.

➤ If any of the numbers are the same, roll one of the cubes again. You need three different numbers.

➤ Write six division problems and solve them.

➤ Record the number of zero remainders that you have.

Write six division problems. Use the space below to solve.

(1) _____   (2) _____

(3) _____   (4) _____

(5) _____   (6) _____

Number of zero remainders ⬜

Solve here.

Home Note: Your child divides two-digit numbers.

Division Bingo

DIRECTIONS

1

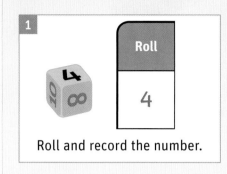

Roll
4

Roll and record the number.

2

Dividend from Bingo Card
24

Choose a dividend and record.

3

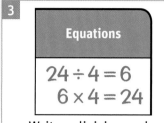

Equations
$24 \div 4 = 6$
$6 \times 4 = 24$

Write a division and a multiplication equation.

Roll	Dividend from Bingo Card	Equations	Roll	Dividend from Bingo Card	Equations

Home Note: Your child plays a game that reinforces his or her understanding of divisibility.

Division Bingo E

16	24	28	32	40
36	42	48	49	54
56	60	FREE SPACE	63	64
70	72	80	81	90
100	36	60	24	24

Home Note: Your child plays a game that reinforces his or her understanding of divisibility.

Math Vocabulary

➤ Write new words and terms in the box.

➤ Write a definition, show an example, or draw a picture for each word or term in your list.

Home Note: Your child records terms and examples of math vocabulary.

Math Vocabulary

➤ Write new words and terms in the box.

➤ Write a definition, show an example, or draw a picture for each word or term in your list.

Math Vocabulary

Home Note: Your child records terms and examples of math vocabulary.

Glossary

divide

When you split a number or separate a number of objects into equal groups, you use the word *divide* to describe what you are doing. For example, if you separate 12 cookies into 3 equal groups (written like this: 12 ÷ 3), you divide 12 by 3.

divided by

We read 12 ÷ 4 = 3 this way: 12 *divided by* 4 equals 3. The symbol ÷ means *divided by*.

dividend

The number being divided into equal groups is the *dividend*. In the equation 20 ÷ 5 = 4, the dividend is 20. 20 is the dividend in the other ways of writing 20 ÷ 5.

$$\frac{4}{5)\overline{20}} \qquad \frac{20}{5} = 4$$

divisible

When you get a zero remainder, you can say that the *dividend* is *divisible by* the *divisor*. For example, 20 is divisible by 5 because the quotient is 4 and the remainder is zero. 23 is not divisible by 5 because there is a remainder of 3 (23 ÷ 5 = 4 R3).

division

Division is the word for what we do when we divide.

division equation

A *division equation* is a number sentence that has two sides separated by an equal sign. Both sides have the same value and there is a division on one or both sides. Examples of *division equations* are 24 ÷ 6 = 4 and 5 = 15 ÷ 3.

divisor

The number you are dividing by is called the *divisor*. For example, in the equation 20 ÷ 5 = 4, the divisor is 5. 5 is the divisor in the other ways of writing 20 ÷ 5.

$$\frac{4}{5)\overline{20}} \qquad \frac{20}{5} = 4$$

equal groups

Equal groups means each group has the same amount. For example, if there are three circles and each circle has 2 stars, then there are three *equal groups* of two stars.

equation

An *equation* is a number sentence that has an equal sign to show that the two amounts on either side of the equal sign have the same value. 12 ÷ 3 = 4 is an equation.

grouping problem

A problem is a *grouping problem* when there are a number of things being put into equal groups and you want to figure out how many groups there are. We can use division to solve a grouping problem. An example of a grouping problem is:

An example of a *grouping problem* is:

> There are 24 students. (number to begin with)
>
> Each relay team will have 6 students. (equal groups)

Glossary

How many relay teams will they make? (number of groups)

24 ÷ 6 = 4, so there are 4 teams.

multiplication

When you write 2 × 3 = ____, you are asking, *How many in all when there are 2 equal groups of 3?* We use the symbol × to show multiplication.

Multiplication is related to division. To solve 28 ÷ 4 = ____, say, *What number times 4 equals 28?* (____ × 4 = 28) Since 7 × 4 = 28, the answer to the division problem is 7. (28 ÷ 4 = 7)

quotient

The *quotient* is the answer to a division question. It answers the question, *How many equal groups of ____ are in ____?*

For example, in 20 ÷ 5 = 4, 4 is the quotient because there are 4 equal groups of 5 in 20. When the answer to a division problem has a remainder, the quotient is the part of the answer that does not include the remainder. In 20 ÷ 6 = 3 R2, the 3 is the quotient.

4 is the quotient in the other ways of writing 20 ÷ 5.

$$5)\overline{20}^{\,4} \qquad \frac{20}{5} = 4$$

remainder

When we divide, we are finding the number of equal groups in the dividend. Sometimes there are leftovers because there isn't enough to make another group. The leftover is called the *remainder*. For example, the division equation 24 ÷ 5 = ____ asks the question, *How many*

equal groups of 5 are there in 24? There are 4 equal groups of 5 in 24 with 4 left over.

We write the equation as 24 ÷ 5 = 4 R4 and read it as *24 divided by 5 equals 4 remainder 4.*

sharing problem

A problem is a *sharing problem* when there are a number of things being shared equally or put into equal groups and you want to figure out how many will be in each group. We can use division to solve a sharing problem.

An example of a *sharing problem* is:

There are 12 marbles. (number to begin with)

3 friends are going to share them. (number who will share)

How many marbles will each friend get? (how many in each group)

We write it this way: 12 ÷ 3 = ____. Each friend will get 4 marbles.

symbols

You use *symbols* in mathematics to name numbers (12, 308, $\frac{1}{2}$), operations (+, −, ×, ÷), and relationships between numbers (=, >, <, ≈).

symbols for division

12 ÷ 3   ÷ means *divided by.*

$\frac{12}{3}$ The fraction bar is a division symbol. We read this as 12 divided by 3.

$3)\overline{12}$ The partial box is a division symbol. We read this as 12 divided by 3.